FOREWORD

In compiling this book of short pieces, I have not attempted to copy the idiom of the tests used for the Associated Board's Grade 6 sight reading tests, rather to provide pieces of the same degree of difficulty, the last few a little harder than the opening tests – widely contrasted pieces that will give pleasure to all those who play them.

The Associated Board's Grade 6 syllabus does not specify keys, so we should assume that the candidate must be prepared for a test in any key.

For the development of sight reading skills, the best training is daily practice. Of first importance is the rhythmic presentation; the pianist should keep moving forward and not go back to correct mistakes. In practice, of course, these mistakes can be reviewed and a second attempt made.

Many of the examples that follow contain changes of clef, a musical feature that needs quick observation. I do not think it necessary at this stage to list the expression marks and musical terms; students taking Grade 6, having passed Grade 5 Theory of Music, should be familiar with them.

Though I have inserted pedal instructions in several pieces, the Board does not normally do so. My reason for adding them is to show what kind of music can only be effective if the sustaining pedal is applied.

Joan Last

2

4

★ The first trill is written fully.
The others retain the same pattern.